Humphrey's Corner
Sally Hunter

# Baby
# Record Book

Sally Hunter

igloobooks

# igloobooks

This edition published in 2015
by Igloo Books Ltd
Cottage Farm
Sywell
NN6 0BJ
www.igloobooks.com

**www.humphreys-corner.com**

HUN001 0215

2 4 6 8 10 9 7 5 3 1
ISBN: 978-1-78440-269-3

Printed and manufactured in China

This **igloo book** belongs to

.......................................

# Waiting for

Date I was due ..............................................

What I was nearly called

Boy ........—........—........ Girl ........—........—........

What my bedroom looked like

..........................................................................................
..........................................................................................
..........................................................................................
..........................................................................................
..........................................................................................

# Baby

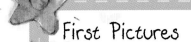

my nursery

First Pictures

## cute and cosy

# My Birth

I arrived at ................... am/pm   on ...........................................

Where I was born ...........................................................

Weight ............................................................................

I was ........................ long ............................................

My hair was ....................................................................

My eyes were ..................................................................

First Pictures

# adorable

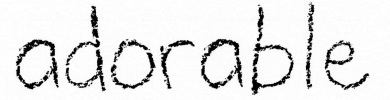

# Coming Home

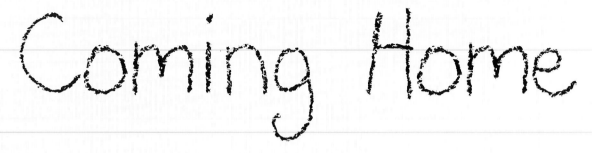

my first picture at home

First Pictures

home sweet home

I came home on

..........................................................

I was wearing

..........................................................

My new address was

..........................................................

I lived with

..........................................................

# My First Visitors

My first visitors were

.......................................................................................

.......................................................................................

.......................................................................................

## I had gifts and cards from

.......................................................................................

.......................................................................................

.......................................................................................

.......................................................................................

.......................................................................................

my family pictures

First Pictures

my family pictures

# Family Tree

Mummy

Brothers and Sisters

Grandparents

Aunties, Uncles and Cousins

Great-Grandparents

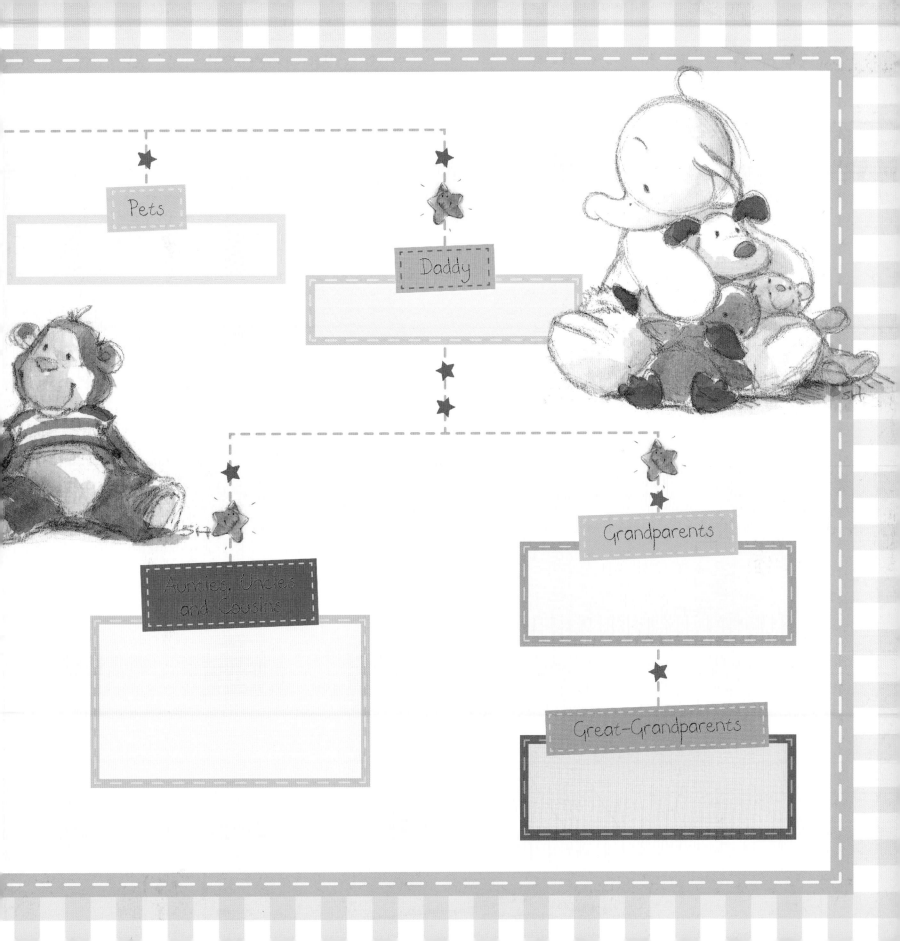

Pets

Daddy

Aunties, Uncles
and Cousins

Grandparents

Great-Grandparents

# My Firsts

I first smiled on .................................................................

I first laughed on .................................................................

I first clapped on .................................................................

I first waved on .................................................................

My first haircut was on .........................

I first sat up on ...........................................

My first handprint

My first footprint

# My Progress

My first tooth came on ..................................................

I first crawled on ..................................................

I first drank from a cup on ..................................................

I used a spoon for the first time on ..................................................

I first wore shoes on ..................................................

I stood upright on my own on ..................................................

My first steps were on ..................................................

I first slept through the night on .................................................................

I first spoke on ...............................................................................................

My first words were ......................................................................................

standing for the first time

First Pictures

standing tall

Progress in

Picture of me at 1 month

Picture of me at 3 months

1 month

3 months

# Pictures

Picture of me at 6 months

6 months

Picture of me at 9 months

9 months

# Things I Like Best

The toy I like best is ...........................................................................

The food I like best is ...........................................................................

The activities I like best are ...........................................................................

The stories I like best are ...........................................................................

The songs I like best are ...........................................................................

The people I like best are ...........................................................................

The place I like best is ...........................................................................

My friends are

..........................................

..........................................

..........................................

..........................................

First Pictures

bestest
friends

First Pictures

friends
forever

# My First Birthday

How we celebrated

..................................................................................

..................................................................................

Who was there

..................................................................................

..................................................................................

Some of the presents I received

..................................................................................

..................................................................................

The presents I liked the best

..................................................................................

..................................................................................

First Pictures

Pictures of my first birthday

happy
birthday

First Pictures

celebrate!

# Special Times

## My most memorable moments

..................................................................................................

..................................................................................................

..................................................................................................

..................................................................................................

My most memorable photo

First Pictures

unforgettable